A Sensational Story

An alliterative retelling of the birth of Christ

Adaptation By
Jon Brooks

Illustrated By
Elisabeth Somerville

The story of Jesus' birth is found in the gospels of Matthew and Luke.
Elements of both accounts were incorporated into *A Sensational Story*.

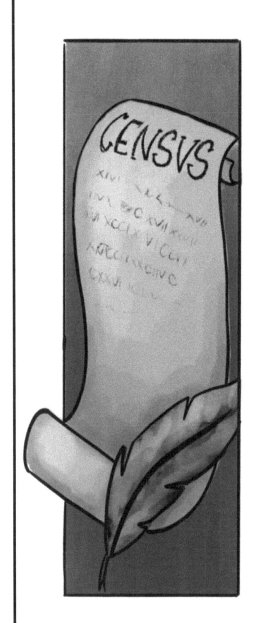

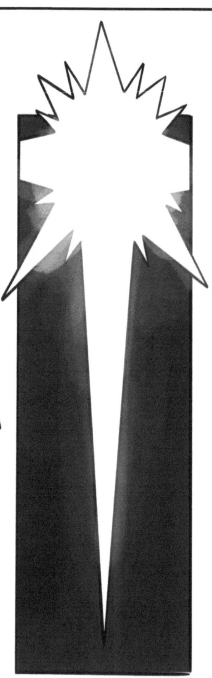

A Sensational Story -- Surprisingly, not some simple seasonal Santa story but a serious and singularly significant saga. Simply stated, it's a sacred story starting with Caesar's census, a celestial serenade, and a shining star.

A seraph said she shall conceive and share a son who shall save sinners. Joseph, still single, said she should silently steal away and sit in stealth to circumvent shame.

"Nonsense, this situation's special," said the seraph. "This son is of the Spirit. Set-off to the city of his surname for the census."

(Caesar's census was started to set a surtax while Cyrenius was overseeing Syria.)

So, in the season when she was showing significantly, they set-off and subsequently saw a city shelter (some shoddy set of suites on the south side).

The snobby staff stated that they were "sans space." "Some simply shan't be staying to sleep." So they sent them shivering outside to seek shelter in a stark stable.

That same silent sacred star-filled sundown, some shepherd's son sitting solo in the sage was suddenly surprised to see a shocking sight. A seraph showed and started a spectacular soliloquy. The shepherd's son shuddered, scared stiff. Stuttering, he summoned sleeping shepherds. Several seraphim showed-up and started ceremoniously singing sacred songs.

"Sing to the Supreme Sovereign in the Stratosphere!
Shalom for this serene satellite in the Solar System & Salutations to its Citizens!"

(silly song)

"Stop stalling, start strolling.
Seek the Savior son *sous* the star."

Simultaneously, somewhere toward Shanghai, several smart sages, seeing the stellar sign, saddled up and set-off on their significant search for the Savior with some special ceremonial celebration selections.

The shepherds, stunned to receive the signal in the sky, sprinted sandal-shod to seek the site of the sleeping son in the city.

They soon saw a snoring sow, some soft-suited sheep and a stout steer sleeping soundly and settled in the security of the stable; and the Son, the Savior, swaddled sweetly and set safely in the soft straw of the steer's stall.

Subsequently, the sages, saddle sore from their sojourn through the sand, stepped from stirrups and stopped to speak to Caesar's satrap. Such a sensation ensued that Caesar's stooge, the city's sovereign, sought to silence this small celebrity.

So, after stopping under the star and serving the Savior celebration stuff such as a shiny substance, a special scent, and a single spice; the sages slipped away in the shadows, sensing civic insincerity.

Some shepherds speculated about the significance of this sacred symbol saying, "This shall set the stage for a supreme sacrifice and sanctification. We should set-out to share the Savior's sensational story from Syria to Swannanoa!"

AUTHOR'S NOTES:

The story of Jesus' birth is found in the gospels of Matthew and Luke. Elements of both accounts were incorporated into *A Sensational Story*. I wrote this, shortly after my son was born, to have a fun re-telling of the Christmas story to share as a monologue at Advent and at Christmas parties. Sometimes, hearing something familiar in a new way allows for fresh insight... so does wrestling with 'S' word synonyms to replace the phrases of a traditional account!

Here are several significant statements:

- A **seraph,** from Ancient Judaism, is a type of celestial or heavenly being like an angel.
- Most translations mention Quirinius as rulling over Syria during the time of the census. Imagine my delite to learn that *Cyrenius* is the form of his name used in the King James translation!
- As a mixed phrase, "***sans* space**" incorporates the French word *sans,* meaning "without."
- *Shalom* is the Hebrew word for a deep abiding peace, so the strange song of the angels translates to the familiar: *Glory to God in the Highest, Peace on Earth, Good will toward men!*
- French comes through again: ***Sous** the Star* uses the French word *sous* meaning "under."
- A **satrap** is an area governor and probably a better way to describe Herod than "**Caesar's Stooge.**"
- The **shiny substance, special scent, and single spice** are indeed gold, frankincense, and myrrh.
- **Sensing civic insincerity** simply means that the wise men realized Herod did not really want to know where the Savior was in order to worship Jesus. Herod saw him as a threat.
- **Swannanoa** happens to be the North Carolina valley where the author and illustrator are from!

Jon Brooks developed a fascination with language from his parents and from stellar English teachers while growing up in Central Virginia. As he and his wife raised their own children, they realized there was only an intellectual upside to using a broad vocabulary and prompting good questions. After graduating with a degree in Religious Studies from Furman University, Jon spent a 30 year career in camp and youth ministry. He currently lives and works as a creative consultant in Black Mountain, NC and serves as the board chair for *Equip International*, a missionary training organization.

A Sensational Story

Visit **asensationalstory.com**

Elisabeth Somerville is an artist and illustrator from Montreat, NC. She graduated from Appalachian State University in 2018 with a degree in Studio Art, and currently lives and works in Providence, RI. While proficient in drawing and painting, Elisabeth's primary focus

is digital illustration. She can often be found in a coffee shop, sipping a *London Fog* and drawing on her *iPad*.

To view her full portfolio visit
www.elisabethsomerville.com

CPSIA information can be obtained
at www.ICGtesting.com
Printed in the USA
LVHW051808121120
671500LV00009B/495

9 781735 653013